The Legends of Paul Bunyan

The Legends of PAUL BUNYAN

ROBERTA STRAUSS FEUERLICHT

ILLUSTRATED BY KURT WERTH

COLLIER BOOKS, NEW YORK

COLLIER-MACMILLAN, LIMITED, LONDON

Library of Congress Catalog Card Number: 65-27805

First Collier Books Edition 1966

The Macmillan Company, New York
Collier-Macmillan Canada Ltd., Toronto, Ontario

Printed in the United States of America

Contents

Introduction

No one knows exactly where or how the legend of Paul Bunyan was born. Some think it is based on the accomplishments of a real person. One writer says Paul originally was a French Canadian named Bunyon who fought heroically in a rebellion in 1837. After the rebellion he ran a logging camp. Tales of his vigor as a logger blended with tales of his valor as a soldier, and he was changed from a man into a legend.

Other Paul Bunyan scholars argue that he never existed, that the stories originated in America, not Canada, and that Paul is the only true American folk hero. They say he came out of the Lake States when logging was at its height there. A few claim Paul can be traced all the way back to the early days of logging in Maine.

When a group of men are kept apart from the rest of society because of their occupation they are likely to shape their own traditions and create unique heroes for themselves. The cowboys did it with Pecos Bill. The loggers, sitting in winter camps cut off from the world for six or eight months at a time, came up with Paul Bunyan.

At first the men might just have told stories of many loggers, who might even have been real. These loggers showed unusual strength or courage or wit in a difficult situation. Later these stories clustered around a single hero and he was named Paul Bunyan.

Wherever the first stories arose, the loggers took them along as they migrated to camps in different parts of the country. Stories about Paul Bunyan have been told from Maine to Oregon and from Michigan to Texas.

The legends first appeared more than a hundred years ago. They were passed by mouth from generation to generation for the first seventy-five years. Then, early in this century, people began writing them down.

Originally the legends were not spun out as a continuous narrative. Someone might mention some fantastic thing that happened the year he logged for Paul three weeks this side of Quebec. Another man might try to top the first with an equally straight face and an even grander lie.

The stories were usually told for amusement, to see who could come up with the tallest tale. Or they were used to awe a tenderfoot or tame a braggart.

In time they not only spread throughout the logging industry but to other occupations as well. There are stories about Paul Bunyan as an oil man in Texas and a soldier in World War I.

The legends of Paul Bunyan have never stopped changing and growing since they were first told. It would not be surprising to someday find a new series on Paul Bunyan in Space. But it would lack reality. If Paul wanted to get around the earth he could just walk, and if he wanted the moon he could reach up for it and pluck it out of the sky. He was that big.

The Legends of Paul Bunyan

1

Little Paul and the British Navy

You would think that when a fellow like Paul Bunyan was born there would be such a holler the whole world would hear it and there would be no mistaking afterward just when and where it happened. But maybe everybody was so busy running around looking for a cradle big enough for the boy that they didn't have time to say anything, so now nobody is sure just where he arrived; and everybody is claiming Paul was born in one state or another or even in Canada.

The Canadians say Paul was born on Prince Edward Island, off the eastern coast. The first time he opened his little baby mouth and cried, all the lifeboats put out to sea. They thought the fishing boats were in distress.

An hour after Paul was born he weighed fifty pounds. He grew so rapidly that all the women on the island worked at their looms night and day but they couldn't weave fast enough to keep him in shirts. There were no buttons big enough for his first little suit, so they had to sew on the wheels of a wheelbarrow.

The only place big enough to christen Paul was the Gulf of St. Lawrence. Some volunteers were lowering him into the Gulf with a crane when the chain broke. Paul hit the water with such a splash there was a tidal wave in the Bay of Fundy.

At least that's what the French Canadians say. Paul himself used to say he was born in Maine, which seems about right because logging was born in Maine too. And as everybody knows, Paul Bunyan invented logging.

From the beginning Paul was too big to sleep in the farmhouse up in Maine, so his folks put him to bed outdoors. But one night he got restless. He rolled over and flattened forty acres of timber.

The people in the village complained so much that Paul's father took all the timber that was already down and built Paul a cradle. He put the cradle, with Paul in it of course, out in the Atlantic Ocean, hoping the waves would rock the baby to sleep. But Paul rolled over in his cradle, as babies often do, and the waves he made swept away three villages along the coast.

Paul's folks saw that the cradle wasn't working too well, so they hollered to him to wake up and wade home. But Paul slept pretty soundly for a baby and he didn't hear them. They were afraid that if he rolled over again some more coastal villages would be swamped, so they called out the American navy. The whole fleet came and fired off all their guns, figuring

the noise would wake Paul up, but the American navy was pretty small then and Paul didn't hear a thing.

So the American navy sent for the British navy and His Majesty's ships fired off volley after volley for seven hours before Paul heard the racket.

When he finally climbed out of his cradle and waded to shore, the waves sank every single one of the British men-of-war. Paul's folks felt pretty terrible about that, so they gave the King of England the timber from Paul's cradle and with it he was able to build himself a whole new navy.

2

Paul Bunyan Finds a Trade

After what happened with the navy, Paul's folks built a special house made of rubber for him and kept him there until he was old enough to go to school. He was pretty good at helping his father out around the farm. He could kick out the potatoes so fast that his father grew three crops a year.

Paul's troubles started all over again when he got to the schoolhouse. When a fellow comes along who's different from the others somebody is sure to turn on him. This time it was the teacher. He just didn't know how to handle the boy.

Of course Paul's size was a problem. He needed four desks and his head stuck up the chimney. His books had to be hauled to school in a cart, and then the teacher allowed him to bring only one a day because the schoolhouse wasn't big enough to hold any more.

Just to write his name Paul had to put five copy books one on top of the other, and even then the teacher would only see part of each letter, so he would mark him wrong.

The real trouble started over a pencil. The pencils the other boys used were so small they would get caught under Paul's fingernail. So he went out into the forest and pulled up a fir tree. Then he stripped off the branches and the roots and sharpened one end.

When he brought his pencil tree to school the next day the teacher got mad.

"Why can't you use a pencil like all the other boys?" he demanded.

"I'm not like the other boys," said Paul. To prove it he picked up the teacher, stuffed him into the stove, and went home. Luckily it was a warm day in late spring and the stove wasn't lit. But Paul's folks knew the boy could never return to school.

"What are you going to do now, son?" asked his father.

"I don't know, Pa," he said. "I'd like to go to work but I can't think of a job big enough for me."

"You're right," said Mr. Bunyan. "There isn't a job in the world big enough for you right now. You'll have to invent one."

Paul went off for a walk to think about it a bit and the first thing he saw was the trees. You can't look in any direction in Maine without seeing the trees. And it came to him all at once.

"I'm big," he thought, "but so is America. I'm tall, but so are the trees. I'm strong, but so are other men. I'll make up a crew of the hardiest, bravest men I can find and we'll go out and chop down the trees so they can be used to build America."

He went back and told his father, and Mr. Bunyan was pleased. "I haven't much to give you to start you off," he said, "but you're bound to need an ox to help you haul logs from the woods. A little ox was born to-day—the same day as the logging industry—and I want you to have him."

Mr. Bunyan took Paul into the barn and gave him a newborn white ox. Paul warmed it in his arms. "Because you are only a baby I will call you Babe," he said.

And with the little ox under his arm Paul waved good-by to his folks and set off into the woods to begin logging.

And that's how Paul used to tell of his birth and boyhood up in Maine.

There's still another story that claims Paul Bunyan was never a baby at all. He was born a full-grown logger with a black mustache and even white teeth and an ax in one hand and a crosscut saw in the other.

And that might be true, too. With a fellow like Paul Bunyan there's no way of knowing.

3

A Full-grown Logger

Even the fellows who argued about where Paul was born would have to agree there never was a man like him.

There's no saying how tall he was because there wasn't anything big enough to measure him against. But he was tall all right. Even the tops of the mightiest redwoods no more than brushed against his belt, and he used young fir trees just to comb his beard.

And strong? Say, he could lift a loaded sled—horses, logs and all—and turn it around in the road so it could go back where it came from.

But strong as he was he was as nimble on his feet as anybody you ever saw. He was the only man in camp who could blow out the lantern on one side of the bunkhouse and be in bed on the other before it got dark.

And he had a great sense of humor too. He could tell when a joke was coming and laugh when it was still ten miles away.

Paul was big and everything about him was big. Bears would hibernate for the winter in his thick beard

and more than one spent the summer there too because every time Paul spoke there was such a cooling breeze.

His watch was so gigantic that once, when Big Ole the Blacksmith opened it to oil the springs, a logger wandered in among the pieces and was lost for three days. Two men worked full time with a scoop shovel just to keep Paul's pipe filled.

When Paul invented logging he had to start at the beginning because nobody had ever logged before. He had to invent everything but the trees. It was he who figured out all the tools and the methods for the first hundred years or so.

Almost everything there is about logging is Paul's work. Because at the beginning there was no logging. There was just Paul and the ox.

4

Babe the Blue Ox

Just as it's true there never was a man—even a logger—who could hold an ax beside Paul, there never was another animal that could measure up to Babe. Paul wouldn't have been half of what he was—maybe even less—if not for the ox.

Though Babe was white when Mr. Bunyan gave him to Paul, he lay about in the drifts the Year of the Blue Snow and after that his hide was colored forever. He was a blue ox for so many years that only the old-timers and their grandfathers could remember back to the days when he was still white.

He was just a baby calf when Paul took him off to the woods, but that sweet Maine air was good for him and he became the strongest animal in the world. He could pull anything that had two ends to it. Sometimes he would even pull some things that had only one end, and that was even harder.

When Paul wanted to strip the bark off a tree he would hitch Babe to one end of the trunk and hold on to the other. He and Babe would give a little tug in opposite directions and the log would come out peeled clean.

Once Paul wanted to move a cookhouse to the other side of the camp. He hitched Babe to it and the ox pulled it over. Then he went back and had Babe haul over the storage cellar.

That was when Babe was still a calf. Later, when he was stronger, he could move the entire camp at once. Paul had the bunkhouses built on sled runners. When it came time to push on to a new camp the men would link all the houses with chains, and then Babe would haul the whole camp to wherever Paul wanted it.

It would be impossible to say just how big Babe was, because nobody ever had the time it would take to measure him right. Johnny Inkslinger, the camp clerk, always used to say that when he got through surveying the whole United States he would survey Babe, but he didn't expect to live long enough to do both.

The closest that anyone could figure was that Babe measured forty-two ax handles and a plug of chewing tobacco between the eyes. Some say Babe measured only seven ax handles, but that means they used Paul's axes. Seven of Paul's were equal to forty-two of anybody else's.

Between the horns Babe was eighty-four ax handles and two plugs of tobacco. On washdays the men would string a line between Babe's horns and hang out their underwear to dry. Once a young crow tried to fly in a straight line between Babe's horns and before he could make it he died of old age.

As close as anyone could guess, Babe weighed 10,000 pounds. This is how they did it. Brimstone Bill, the bullwhacker who was in charge of Babe and all the other livestock, once found an old factory scale big enough to hold one of Babe's hoofs. That hoof weighed 2,500 pounds. Bill then called in Johnny Inkslinger, who multiplied by four and came up with the 10,000 figure. But that didn't take into account Babe's head or tail, and anyway they weighed him before supper, so the figure probably isn't even close.

The lakes in Wisconsin and Minnesota were originally holes made by Babe's hoofs. Not all of Babe's hoofprints filled with water, though, and the ones that stayed dry were even more of a problem than the ones that got wet.

Once a pioneer family on their way west fell into one of those footprints—mules, wagon and all. That hole was so deep that the youngest son, who was a babe in his mother's arms at the time of the accident, was sixty-three years old when he finally climbed to the rim and staggered to the nearest town to tell his dreadful story.

Babe's length has been the subject of much discussion, but no measurements have ever been recorded, probably because no one who ever worked for Paul could count that high. It's true, though, that when Paul stood at Babe's head he had to use a pair of field glasses to see what the ox's feet were doing.

Shoeing Babe was a problem because no one could build an oxsling big enough to hold him. But after

Paul logged off North Dakota there was enough room for Babe to lie down to be shoed. Each time Babe needed new shoes they had to open a new iron mine in Minnesota. Big Ole the Blacksmith had the job of making the shoes. Once he had to carry a set of them to the other side of camp and with every step he sank a foot into solid rock.

Babe's appetite was about right for his size. For snacks between meals he ate fifty bales of hay, wire and all. A dozen men were kept busy every day just picking the wire out of Babe's teeth.

Those were just the snacks, though. For his main meals he ate pancakes just like everyone else at Paul's camps.

All this eating and working naturally made Babe thirsty. Paul never could keep enough water on hand for the ox till he dug the Great Lakes, and then Babe finally had a hole big enough to drink from.

5

Babe Helps Out

Paul always said Babe was the best worker he ever had. There wasn't anything the ox couldn't do. When Paul began logging along the Pacific coast he found a river that was very deep but too narrow for driving the logs down to the sawmill. So Paul hitched Babe to the river and the ox pulled it over on its side, and after that Paul had no trouble at all.

Babe was always a big help when the logging roads weren't too good. Out in Oregon there was a road that was so crooked that when the loggers walked on it they frequently met themselves coming from the other direction.

The teamsters would set out from the woods to the landing with a load of logs, and after a couple of hours on the road they would find they had gone right back to the forest instead of to the camp. Since there were already plenty of logs in the forest, it didn't do anybody much good and it wasted a lot of time besides.

One day Paul said to his foreman, Chris Crosshaul, "This road is giving me a lot of trouble. I'm going to fix it."

"What can you do about a crooked road, Paul?" asked Chris. "Maybe we could build another one right next to it, only straighter."

"No," said Paul. "We'll fix this one. Send Bill and the ox to me. And tell Bill to bring along the strongest chain he has."

In a while Brimstone Bill came up with Babe, and the ox was hauling a big pile of chains.

Paul hitched Babe to the road. Then he gave the command.

"Pull!"

It was a funny sort of job even for Babe, but the ox was willing. He pulled so hard the blue got three shades deeper and a little on the purple side. When he was through, those links of chain had become one solid bar, that's how hard he pulled. But he straightened every kink out of that road. After that you could put a blindfold on and walk down the middle of it without going off at the side even once.

Babe did another big job for Paul the year they were logging on the Little Gimlet River. Paul had a smaller crew than usual and there was just too much forest for them to handle. Besides, the tote roads were bad and the hodags were particularly fierce and hungry that year. The hodag, you know, is one of the most terrible animals of the forest. It eats nothing but young loggers and the only sound it ever makes is a loud "gulp" when it swallows one. Nobody has ever described the hodag because everyone who has ever seen one has instantly died of fright.

Since Paul was losing his men to the hodags when he didn't have enough to begin with, he decided he had to invent a new way of operating.

"The purpose of logging is to get the logs to the landing, right?" he asked Johnny Inkslinger one day.

"Right," said Johnny, who was busy multiplying with one hand, while with the other he divided what he had just multiplied.

"Therefore," continued Paul, "it doesn't matter where the work is done. Instead of sending the loggers into the woods to be eaten by hodags I will bring the woods to the loggers and the hodags can go hungry. They won't dare attack the men in camp."

The next day Paul went out into the woods and hitched Babe to a section of land, which is 640 acres. Babe hauled the section to the landing. There the men chopped the trees down. When the section was clear Babe hauled it back to its place in the woods. That way all the work got done and the hodags had nothing to eat for the rest of the winter but each other.

Babe was helpful all right, and Paul would be the first to admit he couldn't have invented logging without him. But he was also full of mischief. He liked to sneak up behind the spring drive and drink up all the river water, leaving the logs high and dry.

Paul put Babe's fondness for river water to good use, though, the year they logged on the Little Garlic. Chris Crosshaul was foreman then, and Paul told him to take the logs down the Mississippi.

Chris wasn't too bright and he took a mess of logs all the way down to New Orleans before he discovered they weren't Paul's. Paul used to pinch his logs to identify them, and the logs Chris had driven weren't pinched. They carried someone else's mark.

Chris was in trouble then. He didn't know what to do. How could he get the logs back up the river? Well, he sent a message to Paul right away, and Paul knew exactly what to do. He fed Babe barrels of salt until the poor ox was nearly crazy with thirst. Then he led Babe to the upper Mississippi to drink.

Babe gulped the water with such force that he sucked all those logs back upstream faster than they had gone down.

6

The Buckskin Harness

Though Babe was a great worker when he was young, as he grew older he got lazy, which is not uncommon. Brimstone Bill used to say that what ruined Babe, besides all those pancakes he ate, was the buckskin harness.

One day one of Paul's men, a fellow named Forty Jones, spied a herd of deer at a drinking hole in a valley that lay a little below the camp. There was a big pile of logs right above the drinking hole. Forty kicked out the key log and the whole pile crashed down into the valley and killed all the deer.

The loggers had platters full of venison steak for dinner the next Sunday, and Brimstone Bill took all the skins and made a harness for Babe.

The first man to use the buckskin harness on Babe was an assistant cook named Pinkeye Martin. Pinkeye had been ordered to bring in wood for the cookstoves. He hitched a sled to Babe, using the buckskin harness, and led him out into the forest. There Pinkeye loaded the sled with wood. Then he turned Babe around and headed back to the camp.

Just as they set out it started to rain. By the time Pinkeye got back to the cookhouse he saw that though Babe was right beside him the rain had stretched the buckskin so much that the loaded sled was still in the woods.

Pinkeye didn't know what to do, so he told Babe to stay where he was and he went into the cookhouse to eat his dinner. While he ate, the rain stopped and the sun came out, blazing hot. Well, the heat shrank the buckskin. As it came down to its original length it pulled the loaded sled into camp. Babe never had to move.

After the ox saw all the work that could be done without him he never was the same. When Brimstone Bill led him out to the woods to bring in the logs Babe as much as said, "Let the harness do it."

Paul and Bill tried to explain to Babe that you couldn't count on the harness because it might not rain at the right time or it might not dry at the right time. But Babe was stubborn as an ox. Whenever he was hitched up for work you could see him peeking up at the sky to see if it looked like rain.

7

Lucy and Benny

Paul had other livestock too, besides Babe, though you don't hear much about them. He had so many yoke of oxen that he was never able to count them. He also had a cow named Lucy.

Lucy was a funny sort of cow. Brimstone Bill, who knew her better than anyone, always said she was part Jersey and part wolf.

She was pretty dumb, even for a cow. The Year of the Deep Snow, when all the grazing land was covered, Bill put green goggles on her and sent her out to graze in the snow, and she did. The only difference it made was that her milk came out cold instead of warm, so the men used it to make ice cream.

Paul kept Lucy around his camps because she was such a good milker. She gave so much milk a dozen men were busy all the time just skimming off the cream. And it was good, sweet milk that tasted fine in the tea or coffee.

One year, though, there was trouble with Lucy's milk. There wasn't enough good pasture land to graze on, so Lucy ate spruce and balsam boughs instead. Her milk became so strong it curdled the coffee. But Johnny Inkslinger, who always saw to it that nothing was wasted, suggested that it be used for cough syrup, and it was, all that winter.

The butter made from this milk was so tough it wouldn't melt, even on hot bread or pancakes. Paul told the men to save it, and the following spring he used it to grease the logging roads so they could run the sleds all summer.

Paul was often asked if Lucy was the mother of Benny, the little blue ox. She wasn't. Lucy was at the Dakota camp when Paul bought Benny from a farmer in Bangor, Maine.

Benny was called the little blue ox to distinguish him from Babe. Benny was about half Babe's size but he ate twice as much. That's why the farmer sold him to Paul when the ox was just a week old. There just wasn't enough hay to feed him.

Paul hitched Benny behind his sled and set out for North Dakota that same night. The western air was good for Benny. Every time Paul looked around the calf had grown two feet taller.

When Paul finally got Benny to the camp he fed him buffalo milk and pancakes and put him in the barn for the night.

The next morning he went out to see how the new calf was doing. Benny was not in sight.

"Where's Benny?" he asked Brimstone Bill. "He's the calf I brought in last night. I put him in the barn."

"I don't know where Benny is," said Bill. "Do you know where the barn is?"

And then Paul realized that the barn wasn't where it was supposed to be. He and Bill set out to follow Benny's tracks. They led to the cookhouse where Benny was lapping up the breakfast pancakes.

And the barn? It was perched on Benny's back. The little ox had grown that much in one night.

But Benny never did get to more than half Babe's size and he never was a very good worker. While Babe was sometimes mischievous, Benny was just plain ornery. He wouldn't do half the work Babe did and he would never pull a load unless there was snow on the ground. After the spring thaw the only way to get Benny to work was to whitewash the logging roads.

The real reason you never hear as much about Benny as you do about Babe is that he died so young. His appetite was the death of him.

There was no way of keeping him filled with pancakes. All he ate just made him hungry for more. One day he broke into the cookhouse and began bolting down a pile of pancakes lying on top of the stove. In his greed he didn't notice where the pancakes ended and the stove began. So he swallowed the stove too.

It's often said that Benny died of indigestion. That's not true. Benny had the only stomach in the world that could digest a stove and enjoy it too. But the trouble was the damper on the stove was closed. Benny died of smoke poisoning.

They buried Benny a short distance from the camp. The mounds that cover his body are now called the Black Hills of South Dakota.

8

The Man Who Invented Cussing

You always think of Paul's crew as being with him from the beginning. They weren't, though. Paul started logging with just himself and Babe. Johnny Inkslinger and Brimstone Bill and all the rest came later, one at a time. Each of them was as great in his own way as Paul. A man like Paul always draws other good men to him.

There were a lot of other fellows you never hear about more than once or twice, like Curley Charley, who had a double set of teeth and could eat anything. While walking in his sleep one night he chewed up the grindstone.

Jim Liverpool was one of the nimblest of Paul's men. He could jump across a river in three jumps. But Shot Gunderson was the best log spinner. He once twirled a seventy-five-foot log so fast it slid right out of its bark. Then Shot walked ashore on the bubbles.

Joe Muffraw was the assistant cook at most camps. He could leap so high he would write his name on the ceiling with the calks of one boot and erase it with the other.

Sourdough Sam was the boss cook. He made everything except the coffee out of sourdough, which is a yeasty kind of dough that rises.

Chris Crosshaul, who was foreman, wasn't too smart but he had the sharpest eyes in camp. He could see to the tops of the tallest trees in three looks.

Big Ole was the blacksmith. When he struck his anvil the ring could be heard in the next county. Nothing was too difficult for him. With his punch and sledge he would make the holes in Sourdough Sam's doughnuts.

Two of the most important men around Paul's camp, and the two you hear most about, were Brimstone Bill and Johnny Inkslinger.

Brimstone Bill was the boss bullwhacker. He cared for and drove all of Paul's livestock, though none of them were any problem except Benny and Babe.

Bill was famous for his cussing. Nobody knew as many cuss words as he did. He could even cuss in words of one letter, which nobody else has ever been able to do.

It's well known that Bill invented cussing. Before he came along there wasn't anything said that couldn't be heard by little old ladies. In fact little old ladies did most of the talking. But after Bill started cussing it caught on pretty fast, and soon so many people were at it that little old ladies had to wear cotton in their ears and read books with dashes in them.

In his later years Bill wrote a collection of some of his finest cusses and it was published. It is available only to those persons who hit their thumbs with hammers or trip over a pair of roller skates.

Bill came from western Pennsylvania, where he was a schoolteacher. It is believed that he invented cussing while he was still teaching school. At least most schoolteachers think so. Bill used to say he liked bullwhacking better than teaching because at least the oxen couldn't talk back.

Except Benny. Benny was the most ornery and troublesome creature Bill ever had to deal with. He was almost human in some ways.

At the end of a bad day with Benny, Bill had used up every one of the cuss words he knew—and he had used some of them twice. By the time evening came poor Bill was speechless.

When Bill really cut loose, the air around him turned blue. A few people claim that the Year of the Blue Snow it really snowed white but Bill's cussing changed the color. That couldn't be true, though, because Bill's cussing would have melted the snow too and it would have been known as the Year of the Blue Rain.

When Bill cussed mildly he could blister the whitewash off the walls. When he got a little warmer he could singe the bark off a tree. Once he lost his temper and nearly burned down the barn.

While Bill was working for Paul he tried to court a widow back home in Pennsylvania by mail. But the post office refused to deliver his letters after one of them set fire to the mail pouch.

Though Bill had a lot of trouble with Benny, he was really fond of Babe. He cussed at Babe more out of affection than anger. He used to say that he knew the Blue Ox as well as if he had been through him with a lantern.

9

Johnny and the Flipped Flapjacks

Johnny Inkslinger was another kind of person entirely. Even if he had wanted to cuss he would have used numbers instead of words. He would have given every nasty thought a number so that when he got a little mad he might say "Number nine," and when he got very mad he might say "Number 754," and when he got really steaming he might shout "9,326,-845,773,314."

Johnny was a numbers man all the way. If he could have eaten them instead of bread, and drunk them instead of coffee, he would have.

He was really important at camp because Paul had left school without learning anything but how to write his name. When Paul invented logging he had a terrible time ordering supplies and keeping track of the men's hours so he could pay them right. First he tried to keep track of the work time by making notches on a tree. But once a logger who was new at camp chopped down the time tree, and before

Paul knew it his records were floating down the river toward the sawmill.

After that, Paul hired Johnny. From then on Johnny hired the men, kept records of their time, paid them, bought supplies for the camp and sold the men tobacco and clothing. His hobby was surveying, and in his spare time he liked to go out and survey the country.

Johnny invented bookkeeping the way Paul invented logging and Bill invented cussing. He invented all the methods and all the big books with the thin blue and red lines.

Johnny was a great bookkeeper because he could add with one hand and subtract, divide or multiply with the other. He had seventeen sharpened pencils behind each ear and some say he had an eraser fastened to the tip of his nose. That's unlikely, though, because he wouldn't have needed one. He never made a mistake.

There were two things Johnny especially liked to do: invent and save Paul money. Nothing made him happier than to do both together.

He invented the first fountain pen by running a hose from a barrel of ink and putting a point on the end of it. One winter he didn't cross his *t's* or dot his *i's* and he saved nine barrels of ink. After he saw how successful that was he dropped all periods and commas and saved another nine barrels.

To save money on blotters he trained a mouse to roll over the records and soak up the ink. To save his own time he held three pencils in each hand so he could write six figures at once. One year he bought a watch from a peddler that gained so much time it paid for itself in a week.

Johnny always felt his greatest time-saving invention was in the cookhouse. One day he went in to Sourdough Sam and said, "How long do you figure it takes to flip the flapjacks each morning?"

Sam scratched his head thoughtfully with his cleaver and said, "Well, I don't know for sure, Johnny, but we have one hundred and twenty-four men with spatulas in each hand flipping flapjacks from midnight to dawn, and then we only have enough for the first twenty tables."

"Well," said Johnny, "you can put all those fellows on to some other work. Instead of using men to flip flapjacks, put a kernel of corn along the edge of each one. When it's done, the corn will pop and flip the flapjack over."

That's what Sourdough Sam did and it worked fine. Johnny was always especially proud of that idea because it wasn't strictly in the bookkeeping line and it showed he could invent and save money anywhere.

10

Mrs. Paul and the Children

There seems to be some disagreement about whether there was or wasn't a Mrs. Paul Bunyan. It's kind of hard to understand why. No one who had ever seen her could doubt that she existed.

She wasn't one of those dainty little ladies from the East. She was a bull of a woman, almost as big as Paul himself. It kept the plantations in the South busy for seven years just to grow enough cotton for one of her skirts, and then it was too small. She sent it back and some say that's what started the Civil War.

She liked silk blouses, but there weren't enough worms in Japan to make her more than one every dozen years or so. For a belt she wore the equator.

Mrs. Bunyan was Paul's first cook, and she was a good one, too. She invented the soft-nosed pancake and the doughnut with two holes, one on each side. Before she came along doughnuts had holes on only one side. This caused a lot of problems at camp. If the doughnuts were put on the table upside down, the men couldn't see the hole. Then they would complain there were no doughnuts for breakfast, and they liked doughnuts. In fact they liked them almost as much as pea soup. Later on, after Mrs. Paul left and Sourdough Sam took over, he tried to make doughnuts out of pea soup, but it didn't work because the peas clogged the holes.

Anyway, when the doughnuts still had only one hole Paul had to hire an extra thirty-seven men just to turn over the ones that had landed on the table hole-side down. It was a big waste of money and that's why Mrs. Paul got the idea of making all doughnuts with holes on both sides. That way the loggers knew what they were getting no matter which way the doughnuts fell. And once when one of them did fall, it sheared off three of Pegleg Martin's good toes.

Nobody knows exactly when Paul wooed and wed Mrs. Paul. He once said to Sam that it was easier to fell one of those redwoods than to sweep Mrs. Paul off her feet, which seems likely because Mrs. Paul was the heavier of the two. It seems Mrs. Paul originally had her hat fixed for Pecos Bill but every time she sat on one of his horses she squashed it clear down to China. That made Pecos pretty sore and he realized he would lose a lot of horses that way, so he shipped her north to Paul, who was happy to have her. She was a good worker, and with her around the camp he didn't need so many yoke of oxen.

Mrs. Paul stayed up at Paul's camps until he bought Benny, the little blue ox who ate twice as much as

Babe. Right away Paul saw he couldn't feed Babe, Benny and Mrs. Paul all at the same time, so he shipped Mrs. Paul to his folks' farm back in Maine. By then she had had the two kids, Jean and Teeny, and Paul figured a logging camp wasn't a fit place to bring up children. Because Mrs. Paul was up at the Maine farm so much of the time the story grew that she didn't exist.

You don't hear too much about Paul's children because they never did amount to much. When Jean was only a year old he crawled out of his cradle one night and scraped the legs off his pa's bed with a crosscut saw. Paul was pleased. "My boy's going to be a mighty logger someday," he boasted.

But as it turned out, Jean didn't care much for logging. When he grew up he became a salesman. He sold tobacco juice to people who were too lazy to chew their own.

Teeny was different. When she was about sixteen or so she came back to Paul's camp to help him out. She took care of the chickens that laid the eggs for the pancakes. Those eggs were so big it took seven chickens working together to lay just one of them. Teeny had to bend each egg in the middle to get it through the cookhouse door.

Teeny was almost as clever at farming as her pa was at logging. Some folks believe the eggs she brought to the cookhouse weren't laid by hens at all. They came from the eggplant, which only Teeny knew how to grow.

The year Paul logged on the Big Onion, Teeny

crossed an eggplant with an onion plant and a breadfruit tree. That way she grew egg-salad sandwiches, which the men had for lunch every day with their pea soup.

Of course it wasn't easy to grow breadfruit up there in the north woods. That kind of plant grows only in a warm, wet climate. But it was wet enough, all right, because that was the Year the Rain Came Up from China.

You know how rain usually falls from the sky down your collar? Well, this rain fell from the ground up your sleeves.

It rose about ten feet or so and then fell back down to earth. That way it wet you coming and going. Puddles formed in the middle of the air, and if a logger didn't look where he was going, he might walk into one and get his beard soaked.

The men got mad about being wet all the time, but no one got madder than Brimstone Bill. That rain kept putting out the fire in his cusswords. The madder he got, the more he cussed; and the more he cussed, the harder the rain worked to damp him down. That Chinese rain is wetter than most other kinds, you know.

With all that fire and water mixing, pretty soon you couldn't see Bill because of the steam. Finally Paul trapped it in a boiler and sold it to the railroad people, and they had enough to run the first locomotive clear out to California.

11

The Camp on the Big Onion

Paul's camp on the Big Onion was the greatest he ever had. By then all his crew was together—Sam and Johnny and Brimstone Bill and the others.

That year Paul had the largest crew in the history of logging. They ran out of loggers in the United States and Canada and had to bring them over from Sweden; that's how many men Paul hired.

Paul himself never knew how many men he actually had working for him. Not even Johnny Inkslinger could count them all. At first he thought of counting the pancakes and dividing them by twenty, figuring that was about what each man averaged. But every time they had the pancakes stacked for counting, Benny would come along and sweep them up with one or two great swipes of his tongue. So that didn't work.

Finally Paul just gave up trying to count either the pancakes or the men. When someone asked him how many men worked for him the year on the Big Onion, he would just say, "Enough."

Trying to feed and sleep so many men was no small problem. The bunks had to be stacked one atop the other, and the top ones were so high that by the time the men came down for breakfast it was already suppertime in the cookhouse.

Paul borrowed some rails and crossties and he ran a track up the wall of each bunkhouse, across the ceiling and down the other side. But before the engine had delivered the men to their bunks for the night along one wall, it was time to pick them up and bring them down for breakfast along the other.

To call the men in for lunch at noon Big Ole the Blacksmith built an enormous horn.

"What's the good of it?" asked Sourdough Sam. "Nobody here is big enough to blow it."

"Paul is," said Ole, and he went back to punch more holes in the doughnuts.

The first time Paul blew the horn the wind flattened ten acres of pine trees.

"What do I do now?" he asked Ole. "If I keep blowing down trees there will be none left to log."

"Try blowing the horn straight up," Ole suggested. "You can't do any harm that way except maybe scatter a few clouds."

Well, Paul blew straight up and it caused a cyclone. There were such severe storms at sea that all the shipowners banded together and demanded that Paul never blow the horn again. So after all of Ole's work the horn had to be scrapped. It was finally shipped east, where it was made into the roof of a railway depot in one of the large cities.

After that Paul invented the lunch sled so lunch could be carried to the men in the woods and they didn't have to be called back to camp any more. But the men were working so far from the camp that the sled had to start out two weeks ahead of time.

There was only one thing that could rouse the men out of bed in the morning. That was the smell of Sourdough Sam's pancakes. The griddle was so big that no one could see to the other side of it. Ole made it out of some old ironclads melted down after the Civil War. He had to use both northern and southern ships because one side alone just didn't have enough.

The pancake batter was mixed in huge tanks and poured onto the griddle with hoses. But first the griddle had to be greased. Four hundred assistant cooks, or cookees as they were called, skated across the surface with sides of bacon tied to their feet. When the griddle was well greased a net hauled the cookees up to the ceiling so they wouldn't drown when the batter came gushing down.

This was before Johnny thought of putting corn kernels in the pancakes so they would turn themselves over. When they were brown on one side the sourdough made them rise to the ceiling, where the cookees in the net caught them, turned them over and dropped them back on the griddle, being very careful not to miss and hit one of the men below.

Being a cookee working on the pancakes was considered even more hazardous than logging. The worst accident that ever occurred in the cookhouse was when Sourdough Sam, who was nearsighted, mixed some dynamite in the pancake batter instead of flour.

When that dynamite hit the hot griddle there was a roar that was heard up in Alaska. The cookees were blasted through the roof and some of them shot up so high they didn't get back until the next day.

Everything about the cookhouse was gigantic. Any man that had to walk from one end of it to the other took along a week's supply of food.

More than 120 acres of land had to be cleared each week just to supply enough wood for the cook-stove. Several cords of wood were needed for kindling, and the draft was so great that the boy who fed the fire had to have weights in his boots so he wouldn't be drawn up the chimney. He used the heaviest things he could find in camp, which were Sourdough Sam's biscuits.

Feeding all those men had to be carefully planned. The cookees who served the meals wore roller skates and even then each one had only a small part of the table staked out as his territory.

To keep the salt and pepper shakers filled men sped up and down the center of the tables in carriages drawn by four-horse teams. The doughnuts were brought in strung along poles carried over the shoulders of the strongest cookees. They were set up at the heads of the tables and rolled down. The men would spear them as they came by.

The stoves for baking the breads were immense. Once Sam put a bread in the oven and before he had walked around to the other side to take it out it had burned to ashes. The breads themselves were so huge that after the men ate the soft insides the crusts were used as bunkhouses.

To provide water for the morning tea and coffee was no easy task. The well outside the cookhouse was so deep it took the bucket a full day to fill, and the men had to work a full week to haul it back up.

The supply cellars were pretty big too. Once a cookee got lost betwen the flour bin and the potato room and it was two weeks before anyone found him.

But none of the food was ever wasted. Logging burns up a man's energy and builds a man's appetite. One day a logger visiting from another camp was surprised to see a team of horses draw up in front of the cookhouse with a wagonful of what looked like huge logs. As he watched the cookees unload the wagon he commented that the cookhouse was a funny place to store timber. "Why don't you take these logs right to the landing?" he asked.

"They're not logs," replied one of the cookees. "They're sausages for tomorrow's breakfast."

12

Prunestones and Coffee Grounds

Along with pancakes and sausages for breakfast the men usually had cereal, bread, prunes and coffee or tea.

The year Paul logged on the Big Onion the prunestones and coffee grounds got to be the worst of his problems. And the eggshells too.

At first everybody just let the prunestones pile up outside the cookhouse window. Then the chipmunks started to eat them. Paul didn't mind that a bit because he got rid of the prunestones and fed the chipmunks at the same time. But soon the chipmunks began growing. And one night a logger who had been in the woods a little later than usual came in and swore he had seen one of those chipmunks kill a wolf.

Everybody laughed and thought maybe he had been drinking what he shouldn't have. Then word started trickling in from the nearest villages. The settlers were thanking Paul because the chipmunks were killing off all the wolves and now their chickens and cows were safe.

So Paul kept feeding the prunestones to the chipmunks, feeling he was doing everybody a good turn. But then one day he got a messsage from the settlers that the chipmunks were carrying off the cows and some of them had even attacked the cabins. The settlers began to shoot them, thinking they were tigers.

Paul knew he couldn't get rid of prunestones any more by feeding them to the chipmunks. So he had the men take a batch of them and build a bridge across the western end of Lake Superior to a logging camp in Canada. It kept the prunestones away from the chipmunks and shortened the trail by fifty miles.

But that didn't take care of the eggshells and coffee grounds. First Paul had seven men with seven wheelbarrows carting them away from the cookhouse but they couldn't work fast enough. So Paul set up two steam shovels, and all they were able to do was keep a path clear just so the men could get in and out.

Finally that didn't work fast enough either, and pretty soon the men couldn't see whether the sun was up or down because the piles of eggshells and coffee grounds had grown so high.

Paul thought about it alone for a while and then he called in Johnny and they thought about it together. Johnny did some figuring and he figured that if the coffee grounds and eggshells kept piling up, then pretty soon Paul wouldn't have to invent any more mountains. They discussed it and Paul decided that he needed so many men just to clear away the waste from the cookhouse that soon he would have nobody left to do the logging. So rather than try to clean up the camp he figured it would be simpler just to move to a new one.

And that's what they did, and that's why the camp on the Big Onion finally broke up.

But before it did, Paul made one of his most useful inventions. It started one day when he noticed that some of his loggers were looking awfully thin.

Now Paul was one of the kindest bosses in the business, and one of the reasons so many men came to work for him was that he treated them so well. He was especially proud of the fact that he fed his crews better than any other logging boss in the country.

So he stopped one of the fellows that had started to go scrawny and asked him what was wrong. "I'm afraid I haven't been eating much, Paul," said the logger, looking a little embarrassed.

"Why not?" asked Paul. "Isn't the tea strong enough to float an ax? Aren't the pancakes thick and steamy? Don't the sausages snap when you bite into them?"

"I don't know," said the logger. "I haven't eaten any lately. There are just so many men in the cookhouse that there isn't time or place to feed us all. The last time I ate was when I speared a doughnut rolling down the table. And I was so weak I could hardly hold on to it."

Paul was very upset when he heard this. First he took the logger in and fed him from his own plate. Then he called in Johnny and Sam. They calculated for a while and it was plain and true. The logger was right. There were just so many men in camp it was impossible to feed them all at the same time.

So Paul invented the shift system, which is still in use today all over the world. In Paul's camp it worked this way. He divided the men into three shifts. One-third were always going to work, one-third were always working, and one-third were always coming from work. That way everybody got fed, though it kept the cooks pretty busy. They were always making breakfast for some, lunch for others, and dinner for the rest.

Paul even invented the aurora borealis so one shift could work at night. But he had to give that up because the lights just weren't dependable.

13

The Seven Axmen

Everybody knows Paul Bunyan logged off North Dakota. You can prove it because there are hardly any forests left in that state.

Paul did it with one of the smallest crews he ever had. In fact it was made up mostly of the Seven Axmen. Everybody else in camp did nothing but feed them and help them keep their axes sharp. And that was no small job.

Sourdough Sam needed ninety-three cookees to help him feed the Seven Axmen. A two-thousand-pound hog could barely provide enough bacon for their breakfast, and 360 hens died of exhaustion just trying to keep them supplied with eggs. That was before Paul's daughter Teeny invented the eggplant and hens still had regular work.

Nobody is sure exactly how big the Seven Axmen were. They weren't as big as Paul, of course, but they were no ordinary loggers either. They kept a cord of four-foot wood on the dining table just to use as toothpicks.

Paul made each of them a rope-handle ax like his

own. Some say he did it because he had lost so many regular wood handles to the ax-handle hound. That was a funny kind of dog with a hatchet-shaped head. He ate nothing but ax handles and it was a big bother to Paul replacing all the handles he devoured.

But Paul didn't invent the rope-handle ax because of the hound. He never put one of those rope handles on an ax used by an ordinary logger. He just used it when someone special came along, like himself or the Seven Axmen.

Paul discovered, soon after he invented logging, that it was a waste of a good arm swing to chop down just one tree. So right away he invented the double-bladed ax and then he could chop down two trees at once. But that still wasn't enough.

So he melted down three hundred axheads and shaped them into one giant one. Then he wove the toughest rope he could find into a handle.

When his ax was ready he went into the woods, leaned back and swung it in a wide circle. With each swing he felled 320 acres of timber.

Nobody knows where the Seven Axmen came from, but as soon as Paul saw them he knew he wanted them for his crew. He made each of them a rope-handle ax like his own, only about half the size.

The Seven Axmen strode across North Dakota twirling their axes as they went, and with every step they brought down 160 acres of timber.

When Paul saw the kind of workers they were he

also invented the grindstone for them. Before that Paul's men had sharpened their axes by rolling rocks downhill and running alongside pressing the ax against the rolling stone. But there were no hills in North Dakota to speak of and certainly none were big enough for sharpening the axes of the Seven Axmen.

So Paul invented the grindstone and the Little Chore Boy, who did all the odd chores around the camp, pretty nearly broke his back turning it. It was so big that every time it rolled around once another payday had come.

The Seven Axmen cleared off all of North Dakota working out of one camp. They walked to work before dawn each morning and walked back when the stars came out.

Each of the Seven Axmen had three axes. As each ax got red-hot from chopping, the axman would reach for another while a couple of helpers carried the heated ax to the river to cool it off so it wouldn't start a forest fire.

Well, working the way they did, the Seven Axmen had North Dakota completely level in one winter. Some say they pulled up the tree stumps with their teeth. When the job was done they walked up the road with their axes over their shoulders and nobody ever saw them again.

Paul was pretty unhappy about their leaving that way because he never had workers like them, before or since. In fact he was hard put after that to figure out a way to equal the amount of work that had been done that one winter. No matter how many men he hired he never again logged off a whole state in a single season, and nobody else has either.

When he saw that ordinary loggers just couldn't come close to the output of the Seven Axmen he tried to invent new methods that would help. That's why he invented the two-man or crosscut saw. Since Paul made it, the first saw was pretty big. In fact it was long enough to span 160 acres of timberland.

It worked well enough in level country because you could cut down a lot of trees with a saw that stretched that far. But it didn't work so well where the country was uneven.

It cut the trees on the hilltops in just the right place but those growing about halfway down got only their tops sheared off and the saw passed clear over the trees growing in the valleys.

So Paul had to invent the small crosscut saw and give up the idea of ever getting the production he had the year of the Seven Axmen unless he did all the work himself.

14

Logging the Pyramid Forty

Another one of Paul's good years was when he logged off the pyramid forty. A forty is just what it sounds like it should be: a forty-acre parcel of land.

When Paul set out, he figured it wouldn't take much more than a day or two and wasn't even worth setting up a camp for. Back on the Big Onion the men had cleared three forties a week just for fuel for the cookstoves.

But Paul was in for a walloping surprise when he saw the pyramid forty. It wasn't like any other. It measured forty acres all right, but that was only at the bottom.

And the bottom was just the beginning. The land rose in the shape of a pyramid. All four sides grew straight into the sky. They met so high up it took twenty men, looking steadily for a week, just to see to the top.

Every bit of that land was covered with good thick pine. Paul's crew set to work, and before the snows had melted they had cleared 125,000,000 feet of timber.

But it wasn't easy logging off the sides of a pyramid. Because the men were working uphill all the time, they soon discovered one leg was growing shorter than the other. So they turned around and worked left-handed till both legs were the same size again. Then it would start all over, with the other leg getting shorter and so they would have to turn back.

There were never any midgets in Paul's camps, but by the time that winter was over some of the men had gotten pretty short. Those that were short to begin with, why, there was nothing left of them but the sound of an ax swinging.

There were some unusually queer animals that lived at the pyramid forty and no place else. One was the pinnacle grouse, which had only one wing. Naturally it flew in only one direction.

Then there was the goofus bird, which flew backward all the time. It didn't want to know where it was going; it wanted to know where it had been. It frequently ran into the pinnacle grouse and the feathers floating down got into the loggers' eyes, so that they couldn't see whether they were chopping at the trees or each other.

There was another silly bird at the pyramid forty but the men didn't mind this one at all. It was the hillside plover, which laid square eggs so they wouldn't roll downhill. The men used to hardboil the eggs and use them for dice.

There were other advantages to working on the pyramid. All the trees grew out of the sides of the pyramid instead of straight up, so the force of gravity helped the loggers chop them down. And when they were down, there was no bother about loading them onto sleds and dragging them to the landing. They just rolled downhill and into the river below, ready to be driven to the sawmill when spring came.

The men started logging at the bottom of the pyramid and worked their way up. But it was so tall that by the time the loggers reached the top, the stumps at the bottom had already sprouted into new trees seventy feet tall. So the men started all over again at the bottom and worked their way back up. And the same thing kept happening. Paul's men logged the pyramid forty three or four times before it was time to move on to the next camp.

15

The Mountain That Stood on Its Head

Some people confuse the pyramid forty with the mountain that stood on its head. That's a serious mistake because they had nothing in common except that Paul Bunyan logged both of them. The pyramid forty was narrow at the top and wide at the bottom. The mountain that stood on its head was wide at the top and narrow at the bottom, which is another thing entirely.

The mountain that stood on its head really was an upside-down mountain. But it didn't start out that way. It was a regular right-side-up mountain when Paul found it and decided there was good timber along its slopes. The trouble was it was too far from a river along which the logs could be floated to the sawmill in the spring.

So Paul told Brimstone Bill to hitch Babe to the mountain and move it over to the river. Babe was feeling a little frisky that day and he gave the mountain such a jerk that it flipped right over. Now it was handy to the river all right, but it presented new problems.

When Paul saw what had happened he decided to log the mountain just the way it was. Because the mountain was upside down, of course, the trees were upside down too. It was a pretty upside-down year all around, and some of the men figured it was a pity that that wasn't the Year the Rain Came Up from China. Then the loggers could have stood on their heads and everything would have been all right.

Since it was impossible for even Paul's men to log off an upside-down mountain, he had to invent a solution. He got out his old double-barreled shotgun and loaded it with sheet iron. Then he went to the foot of the mountain—except the foot was the head, you know—and fired. He fired for two solid days, stopping only to reload the shotgun once or twice. With each blast of sheet iron three thousand trees were sheared off at the stumps. They fell from the mountain sides to the plain below. Their branches were embedded in the soil, and their trunks, cleanly cut off at the roots by the sheet iron, stood straight and tall in the air.

"Now, my bullies," said Paul, "we have a forest to clear."

The men found it somewhat peculiar to chop down trees at the branches, but they went at it with a will. When all the trunks were down and at the landing, Babe walked among the branches and trampled them firmly into the ground.

This was after the buckskin harness, when Babe had started to get lazy. He hadn't worked for more than an hour or two before he decided he needed a rest. So he leaned against the mountain to get some of the weight off his feet for a moment, and naturally there wasn't a mountain in the world that could hold Babe.

It cracked and buckled and with the roar of a thousand thunderclaps it shuddered into dust. Babe was upset about what he had done, and he licked Paul's neck to show he was sorry, but Paul said it was all right since the mountain had made for some mighty pesky logging anyway.

And that's why you can travel anywhere in America and not find a trace of the mountain that stood on its head. But it was there all right, and some of the real old-timers still remember logging it.

16

The Round River Drive

The year of the mountain that stood on its head was just a big headache for Paul all around. After he had finally gotten the mountain logged clean he told his foreman, Chris Crosshaul, to drive the logs down the river to the sawmill.

Chris and the men set out, feeling kind of happy and maybe a little bit lazy too, the way folks do in the spring. Well, they took the logs down, figuring they would come to a town soon enough, but they rode for two weeks and nothing came in sight.

Then one day one of the men cried out that he saw a town in the distance. But when they got close to it Chris said, "That's not a town. It's another lumber camp."

And that's what it was too. The men were kind of sore because someone was logging so close to Paul's territory.

"It's a pretty big camp," said one.

"Almost as big as Paul's," said another.

They rode right by it and kept going. They still didn't see a town, but they felt pretty pleased because the drive was going good. The logs drummed smoothly over the water and there was no jamming.

Well, they rode another two weeks and still there was no town. All they passed was another lumber camp.

"This is even bigger than the first," said Chris. "Paul's going to be sore when he finds out there are two logging camps so near."

"Whoever the fellow is who built this camp, he did it a lot like Paul does," said Pegleg Martin. "The bunkhouses are stacked pretty much the way ours are."

"Let's keep going," said Chris. "We'll tell Paul about it when we get back."

They kept going but still there was no town in sight. Six weeks after they set out all they saw was a third lumber camp.

"This one really is as big as Paul's," said Chris. "Look—they even have an ox as big as Babe."

"And it's blue too," said Pinkeye Martin.

"There couldn't be two oxen as big as Babe and both of them blue, could there?" asked Chris.

"I don't know," said Pinkeye, "but whoever runs this camp is stealing Paul's style and I think you ought to go up there and tell him to stop it and clear out of Paul's territory."

"I think I will," said Chris, and he went swaggering up the hill to tell the man off. And the first person he ran into was Paul Bunyan himself.

"Hello there, Chris," said Paul. "Did you get a good price at the sawmill for the logs?"

"I haven't got to the sawmill yet, Paul," said Chris. "It's been a terribly tiresome trip and the town's nowhere in sight. What are you doing here, anyway? Why aren't you at camp?"

"Why aren't I at camp?" echoed Paul. "This *is* our camp, Chris. Don't you recognize it?"

And sure enough Chris realized it was Paul's camp he had passed three times in the last six weeks. He just hadn't recognized it because after he left Babe had knocked over the mountain that stood on its head.

"By the Holy Old Mackinaw!" cried Chris. "We've been driving those logs round and round in circles. This river has no outlet."

For a while Paul was perplexed. He had never before tried to drive logs down a round river. But then he remembered that before he came along nobody had ever tried logging either, and that cheered him up.

He scratched his beard for a while and finally he said, "If we can't get the logs to a sawmill, let's build our own." So he had Johnny Inkslinger write a letter east to the sawmill people, saying that Paul Bunyan wanted to order one for his camp.

They sent the sawmill all right, all in little pieces

and packed in a dozen freight cars. The railroad carried it as close to Paul's camp as the tracks came, and Babe hauled it the rest of the way.

Paul hadn't expected the sawmill to come in pieces. He was used to doing things in a big way and he couldn't see why such a little thing as a sawmill couldn't be delivered whole. "If I had known the railroad was too small to carry it, I would have sent Babe for it," he said.

There wasn't anybody in camp who knew much about putting sawmills together, but they went at it hard enough and pretty soon the bits and pieces were in place and there was the sawmill.

Paul gave it one of his sharpest looks and frowned. "Too small," he said.

Everyone could see at once he was right. Babe could have swept it away with one swipe of his tail.

"No point in sending back east for an exchange," said Paul. "It will take too long. Let's build a bigger one ourselves."

So the men took the sawmill apart and used the same equipment to build a new one. Some of the pieces they stretched and others they added to. Big Ole the Blacksmith was busy night and day hammering away at all kinds of metal to fill in the gaps.

Well, the second sawmill was big all right. Paul had to put hinges on the smokestacks so the clouds could get by.

But the men made a terrible mistake. They were loggers, not engineers, and when they put that sawmill together again they somehow managed to get it backward. When they fed it logs it didn't work at all. They had to feed it sawdust and then it would turn out logs.

Paul got good and angry. The last thing he needed was more logs, when the landing was already piled high with the ones Chris Crosshaul had driven around Round River for six weeks. Paul tried running the sawmill a day ahead of time, but that didn't change anything. It just turned out more logs.

So Paul crumbled the sawmill into scrap with one solid kick of his boot. He knew he would have to invent some other way of getting the logs out of Round River.

Paul sent Johnny Inkslinger out to survey the land surrounding the river. "We've got to get these logs out of here somehow," he told him.

When Johnny came back he was beaming as though he had just invented fractions. "Paul," he said, "see those hills on the far shore of the river?" Paul said he did.

"On the other side of those hills," Johnny continued, "is another river that leads right to the sawmill. All you have to do is get the logs over the hills and your troubles are over."

Some men might have been a little discouraged at the idea of driving logs over the hills, but not Paul. "Sam," he said to the cook, "mix up a good, firm batch of sourdough. There has to be enough of it to fill the watertank."

Sam got all the cookees together and they went to work in a hurry. Nothing pleased Sam more than using sourdough for construction purposes. Other doughs might be easier to digest, but with sourdough you could change the face of the earth.

Filling the watertank with sourdough was a task for a dedicated man. Nobody had ever measured it because, like Paul and Babe, it was too big. Johnny Inkslinger figured that if he lived long enough to survey the United States and Babe too, he would then take on the watertank.

Sam and the cookees worked at mixing sourdough twenty-six hours a day for more than a month. Finally the watertank was full.

Paul hitched Babe to the tank and the ox hauled it to the shore of Round River. Then Paul tipped over the tankful of sourdough.

When the sourdough hit the water it began to seethe and foam. And then the river began to rise. It rose until it was level with the surrounding hills. Then the streams of sourdough went pouring over the hills to the river on the other side, carrying along the tremendous pile of logs.

Paul's men had been through many spring drives, and some of them mighty queer ones too. But even the oldest among them had to admit they had never ridden logs over hills on a stream of sourdough. In fact if they hadn't been there they wouldn't have believed it could have happened.

17

Elmer, the Reversible Dog

You hear so much about Paul Bunyan as a logger that most people probably don't realize he was pretty fine at a lot of other things too. He was one of those fellows who, no matter what he does, does it the way everybody else wishes they could.

Take hunting, for example. If Paul had hunted full time instead of logged, he would certainly have been known as the greatest hunter that ever lived.

The first time he went hunting, though, he spoiled it for himself. He was only about six or so and still on the farm in Maine when he went to his father and asked if he could have the shotgun that day.

"Well, Paul," said his father, looking straight up at him, "you can borrow it but you've got to promise to be careful and not hurt yourself."

"I promise, Pa," said Paul. "What do you want me to shoot for supper?"

"I don't much care, son," said Mr. Bunyan. "Ask your ma what she's fixing to have."

So Paul asked his mother and she told him she was hungry for a good venison steak but it would be all right if he just brought in a dozen or so rabbits because it was only his first time with the shotgun.

Paul went out but he didn't waste his time going after rabbits. He wanted to get that venison steak his mother said she was tasting. And he could taste it too, roasted with a pile of chestnuts.

Paul walked about twenty or thirty miles into the woods and finally he saw a deer about five miles ahead. Right away he raised his shotgun and aimed and fired. But the trouble was Paul was too anxious. The moment he fired he ran right toward the deer to see if he had hit it. But, you know, he ran faster than the shot. He got directly in front of it and it hit him squarely in the seat of his trousers.

Paul got good and mad about that, but the deer thought it was so funny that he laughed himself to death, so Paul and his folks had their venison steak that night anyway.

When Paul grew older, he sometimes didn't have to shoot at the animals at all. He just hollered them to death. He would stand back and bellow, and wolves and coyotes would die of fright. Once Paul yelled at a pair of black bears and they got so scared they turned white and lit out for the North Pole. Now all their descendants are white and they're called polar bears.

Paul wasn't just a great hunter. He was great on the trail too. Once he found the bones of a moose that had died of old age. Not having anything special to do that afternoon, he trailed the moose back to the place where it was born.

Of course a hunter like Paul needed a pretty unusual dog to keep up with him. Every step Paul took covered twenty-seven feet or more, and that was when he was just ambling. When he really was in a hurry he could step clear over one of the smaller states like Vermont or Pennsylvania. You can see that a dog would have to be pretty lively to keep at Paul's heels and not feel winded.

Paul liked dogs and he always had a pack of them around his camps. Some of them he trained to hunt mice. Hunting mice at Paul's camp wasn't as easy as you think, because the mice ate scraps of pancakes and they grew as big as bears.

A dog named Elmer was Paul's favorite. But every time Paul took him on even a short hunting trip covering maybe two or three states poor Elmer would limp back with his legs so bowed that Benny could walk between them.

One night after an especially hard hunt Paul was lying in his bunk when Elmer crawled in to get some liniment to rub on his sore feet. Paul heard the noise, and not being awake and not being asleep, he thought it was mice. He grabbed his ax and flung it. It hit Elmer in the middle and sliced him cleanly in half.

As soon as Paul saw what he had done he hollered for Johnny Inkslinger, who was the camp doctor as well as everything else. The sound of Paul's voice knocked all the loggers out of their bunks and the people in the cities nearby stayed home that night, thinking there was a thunderstorm coming up.

Johnny didn't know what had happened but he did know that Paul wouldn't have hollered so loud at that time of night unless there had been an accident or Paul had found a mistake in his figures. Johnny knew his figures were perfect, so he brought all his bandages and ointments figuring someone had been hurt.

And poor Elmer certainly was hurt. There he lay on the bunkhouse floor, one half of him looking up with sad brown eyes and the other half weakly wagging its tail.

"What do I do, Johnny?" asked Paul. It was one of the few times in his life he was so upset he couldn't think.

"Let me figure for a minute," said Johnny. He grabbed a pencil from behind his ear and immediately began to write down numbers and fractions and decimal points as fast as he could. When he finished he said, "I figure we ought to put both halves together again."

So he and Paul jammed the two halves of Elmer together, and Johnny put a mixture of iodine and wood glue around the edges. Then he wrapped Elmer from his ears to his tail in 147 yards of bandages.

"That's all we can do tonight," he announced

when he was through. And everybody including Elmer went to bed.

Before daybreak Paul rolled out of his bunk to see how Elmer was. The dog sprang up when he saw Paul and licked his face, for he was completely cured. But later when Johnny came in and he and Paul took off the bandages they saw they had made a dreadful mistake.

It was dark in the bunkhouse when they jammed the two halves together, and they had done it so quickly they hadn't noticed that one half was up and the other half was down. Elmer's front legs were on the ground where they belonged, but his hind legs were standing straight up in the middle of the air.

It was too late to take Elmer apart again and fix him the right way because the glue had already dried. From that time on Elmer was known as the reversible dog.

And the funny thing was that after that, Elmer became the best hunting dog in the world for Paul. First he would run on his two front legs and then when he got tired he would just flip-flop over and run on his two hind legs. That way he could keep right up with Paul and never get tired.

18

The Siege of Mosquitoes

Day began in Paul Bunyan's camps the way it began in most lumber camps. One of the cookees cried, "Roll out or roll up, my bullies! It's daylight in the swamp!" After a hearty breakfast the men trooped off into the woods to work and didn't return till sundown.

The summer Paul logged on the Little Sawdust River he had only a small crew. In fact there were so few men they were able to work in one shift. Paul didn't have to use the three-shift system he had invented the year on the Big Onion.

When there was only one shift it meant, of course, that all the men left for work at the same time. Well, one morning the crew hadn't been gone more than an hour or two when they came tramping back through the woods. Paul was in his bunkhouse trying to figure out whether there had ever been an Atlantic Ocean drive and whether he should attempt one, when he heard them coming.

He rushed out of the bunkhouse, pretty mad. He treated his men well, but in return he expected a full day's work from them.

"Why are you back so early?" he asked Chris Crosshaul.

"It's not early, Paul," replied the foreman. "Can't you see the sun's gone down already?"

Paul looked up. Chris Crosshaul was right. The sky was black as Sourdough Sam's coffee.

"It's black up there but it couldn't be night already," said Paul. "You just left the camp an hour or two ago. I'll prove it. Where's Sam?"

"Here, Paul." Sam had heard all the noise and had come out of the kitchen to see what was happening.

"What time is it, Sam?" asked Paul Bunyan.

"Well, half the cookees are still wheeling away the prunestones from breakfast, so the men couldn't have eaten more than two hours ago. The other half are still packing up the lunch sled. As far as I can figure it's about half past breakfast or no later than a quarter of lunch."

"Sure is funny," muttered Chris. "If it's that early, why is it so dark? It isn't raining or snowing or anything like that."

Everybody looked up at the sky for a while.

"If it's night," said Sam, "where are the stars?"

"Another thing," said Paul, who was closer to the sky than anyone else, "do you hear that funny buzzing up there? It sounds like a million saws working at once. Chris, you have the sharpest eyes in camp. Aim them up at the sky and don't look back down again till you can tell us what's going on."

The foreman leaned back while two of the loggers supported him and he stared straight up with both his keen eyes. It took him two and a half looks and then he turned to Paul and said, "It's not night at all. Something is flying overhead and blotting out the sun."

"Give another look, Chris, and tell us what it is," said Paul.

Chris looked again, as hard as he could, and then his jaw dropped down to his boottops, he was so surprised by what he saw.

"By the Holy Old Mackinaw," he said, "it's a herd of mosquitoes."

"Mosquitoes!" said Paul, and everybody else, though not quite so loud.

"Mosquitoes," said Chris. "And they are the biggest mosquitoes I've seen since I was born and before that too."

"How big can a mosquito be?" asked Paul doubtfully.

"Wait till you see them," said Chris.

Paul saw them the next day and then he knew how big a mosquito can be. Two of them had just killed and eaten one of his oxen and they were sitting on a fence picking their teeth with the thighbones.

Paul killed them with his ax but it was like chopping down a redwood. And that was only the beginning. Paul told Brimstone Bill to keep all the livestock locked in the barn so the mosquitoes couldn't get at them. This went for all the animals except Babe of course. There was no barn big enough to hold Babe, but on the other hand there was no mosquito big enough to hold him either, so he was all right.

Once the livestock was safely locked in the barns the mosquitoes began going after the loggers. One would fly down and try to carry off a logger, and then all the logger's friends would hold on to him so he couldn't be taken away, and then all the mosquito's friends would come along and try to help *him*; and so the men ended up playing tug-of-war with the mosquitoes when they should have been chopping down trees. And worse, sometimes the loggers lost.

Paul ordered the men to stay in the bunkhouses for protection, but the mosquitoes were so fierce they tried to tear the shingles off the roofs to get at the loggers.

And one afternoon the men heard the most awful screeching and buzzing. Fearfully they peered out the bunkhouse windows. The mosquitoes had figured out how to use the grindstone. One of them was turning it and the others were all lined up in a row waiting to get their stingers sharpened.

Well, Paul knew he would have to do something or there would be no logging at all that summer. So he called in Johnny and Chris and Sam and some of the others and asked for ideas.

It was Johnny who came up with the only one that seemed to make any sense. "Let's get a flock of bees in from the Gulf coast," he suggested. "They'll kill off all the mosquitoes for us."

"Then what will we do with the bees?" asked Paul.

"We'll worry about them later," said Johnny, who, like most great thinkers, could handle only one great thought at a time.

Paul agreed to the idea and Johnny ordered the bees. They came roaring into camp a few days later, each one with a sticker addressed to Mr. P. Bunyan, Little Sawdust River Camp, North Woods, U.S.A.

"Okay, Johnny," said Paul. "Tell them to get the mosquitoes and get them good."

At first the bees went after the mosquitoes as though they hadn't eaten for a month, and some of them probably hadn't. But after a while the two pests decided they had a lot in common. They started to get really friendly and some of the bees went ahead and married some of the mosquitoes.

Their children, if you can call them that, were a sight to scare even a hodag. They inherited a stinger from each parent, so there was one in front and one in back. That way they could get the loggers coming and going. Some of these combination bee-squitoes later married fireflies. Their children were really a terror. They could see to sting people night and day.

Well, the plague of insects lasted almost all summer and Paul's men got practically nothing done.

What finally got rid of the pests was nothing Paul did. Toward the end of the summer a fleet of freighters sailed across Lake Superior to bring Paul's camp the fall supply of sugar and molasses.

The bee half of those insects smelled the sweets coming and the whole herd took off across the lake. They attacked the ships and sank every one of them but it was their Waterloo. They lapped up all that sugar and molasses and got so heavy they fell into the lake and drowned.

By then Paul's men didn't have much time left to do some logging and get the drive down the river before it froze for the winter. But Paul helped out, and then they were able to get the whole summer's work done in a week.

19

The Pea Soup Lake

There just wasn't anything Paul's men liked to eat as much as pea soup. Especially the French Canadians. They could eat it nine days a week and fifty-seven weeks a year.

Sourdough Sam kept caldrons of it boiling all the time. The caldrons were so tremendous that instead of throwing in ham bones for flavoring Sam threw in whole hogs. A paddlewheel steamer was used to stir the fragrant mixture.

One day Sam went to Paul with the look of a man in trouble.

"What is it, Sam?" said Paul. "You're bluer than Babe."

"Paul," said the cook, "we're running low on peas. We may not have enough to last the winter. And the men would get pretty mad at me if that happened."

"You bet they would," said Paul. "If you run out of peas the men might throw you in the soup instead."

"I'd spoil the taste," said Sam.

"The men wouldn't know that until it was too late,"

said Paul, "and I'd have to go out and hunt up another cook. Let's not take any chances, Sam. I'll order some more peas."

This was before Johnny Inkslinger had joined the crew and Paul had to do the ordering himself. Since he left school before he learned to read and write he had to draw pictures of what he wanted. This was often a problem. Once he ordered a grindstone and got a Wisconsin cheese instead.

This time Paul sat down with his pen, which was the trunk of a pine tree, and dipped it in some ink that had been melted down the Year of the Blue Snow. Then he carefully drew the smallest circles he could.

"Do you think they'll know they're peas?" asked Paul, who was always a little embarrassed by his inability to write properly.

"They look like cannonballs to me," said Sam.

"The pea factory doesn't sell cannonballs," said Paul. "But to be sure I'll color them green." So Paul mixed the blue snow with a little sunlight and colored the circles.

Well, the pea factory knew what Paul wanted, not because of his drawing but because he was their biggest customer. They sent out a tote teamster with a wagonload of peas first thing.

The tote teamster was moving his oxen along at a good pace when he came to a huge lake just the other side of Paul's camp. The lake was frozen solid, though, so he clucked to his oxen and they headed straight across. Well, that lake was so big that though it was winter when the teamster started to cross it, spring had come before he got to the other side.

When the weather got warm the ice thawed of course, and the teamster, the oxen and the whole wagonload of peas went splashing into the lake. The teamster swam to the shore but everything else stayed under.

The teamster made it to Paul's camp and told him what had happened. The whole wagonload of peas was lost.

But Paul wasn't a man to see anything wasted, not when he had a camp full of men starving for pea soup, because, as Sam had feared, the peas had run out. Paul ordered Sam and the cookees to pour barrels of carrots and onions and celery and salt into the lake. Then the men piled up brush all around the shores. When everything was ready Paul set fire to the brush. The fire heated the lake, and the loggers had the best pea soup they ever tasted because it had a fine oxtail flavor.

Even the pieces of splintered wagon that occasionally floated to the top were no bother. The men used them as toothpicks.

After that Paul's men had all the pea soup they could hold. They drank it for breakfast and for supper. In fact they stayed at the same campsite two years more just so they could finish the pea-soup lake. When winter came again, Sam froze the soup around sticks and had them dragged into the woods so the men could have pea soup for lunch too.

Some of the lazy loggers ate it right from the sticks, but the smarter ones scooped out holes in the handles of their axes. They stuffed the frozen pea soup into the holes and the heat of their hands on the handles made the soup piping hot by the time they were ready to eat lunch.

20

Blue Snow, Deep Snow

The weather in this country isn't like it used to be in the days when Paul was logging. Now the seasons come in regular order—winter, spring, summer, autumn—and if it's a little cool in the summer or wet in the spring people get pretty annoyed and talk about going some place else.

But Paul and his crew knew some weather that was worth complaining about. Of course everybody knows about the Year of the Blue Snow, when it snowed blue for seven days and nine nights.

Nobody knows what caused it, and it certainly hasn't happened again. Some folks say it was so cold that winter that the Great Lakes froze solid from the bottom up and the snow turned blue from the reflection of the water. But that couldn't have been the reason because Paul hadn't invented the Great Lakes yet.

It was kind of pretty that year, with fat blue snowmen melting all over the country. And to some folks it was a real boon, because they melted down the snow and made ink out of it. Some of them bottled it and it's still being sold all over the country.

But to most folks it was just a bother. Because of all that blue on the ground you couldn't tell where the land ended and the sky began. People started clomping all over the sky with their big feet and they got muddy blue footprints on those nice white clouds.

Luckily the Pacific Ocean froze over that year, so Paul had Brimstone Bill hitch Babe and Benny to the cart and they were busy all winter hauling regular white snow over from China. After they had gotten the blue snow all covered over, things got back to normal again.

Another winter that was a nuisance to everybody was the Year of the Deep Snow. That wasn't like the Year of the Blue Snow because this was white and it fell much deeper. Everything on the face of the earth was buried under it. In some places it actually came as high as Paul's waist.

You couldn't see any trees at all. All of America looked like North Dakota after Paul had logged it. Paul had to poke into the snow to find the tops of the tallest pines. For a while it looked as though there would be no logging at all that year, but after thinking a bit Paul invented a solution.

He had the men dig down and around all the trees till they were free of the snow. As each tree came clear Paul lowered two men and a saw into the hole.

In the meantime, Brimstone Bill fixed up two pairs

of Paul's snowshoes so Babe could wear them Babe, standing in Paul's shoes, waited on the surface of the snow while the loggers sawed off the trees below. Then each tree was hitched to a long chain attached to Babe, and the ox pulled the trees to the surface.

That way a good bit of logging got done, although some of the camp cranks complained that Paul should have let them stay in their warm bunkhouses because Babe could have done all the work himself. And they were probably right.

21

The Winter of the Two Winters

The Year of the Blue Snow and the Year of the Deep Snow put together weren't as bad as the Year of the Two Winters, or as it's sometimes called, the Winter of the Two Winters.

It happened when Paul was logging along the Little Garlic River. It had been terribly cold all that winter. One day Paul was sitting in the office with Johnny and Sam and Chris when a little yellow light hit the ledger Johnny was working in.

"What's that?" asked Chris Crosshaul.

"I don't know," said Sourdough Sam. "I can't remember seeing anything like it before."

Suddenly Paul's black mustache rose up from his beard as he smiled and shouted at the same time.

"That's sunlight, my bullies! All of you have forgotten what it looks like."

Johnny Inkslinger was a cautious man. He looked in the direction the light came from. Then he took off his glasses, wiped them with a piece of bark, put them back on and looked again. "It might be sunlight," he said, "but let's make sure."

Johnny's way of making sure was with numbers. He added and subtracted and multiplied and divided and then he took the square root of everything. Finally he said, "You're right, Paul. According to my calculations this is the first day of spring and that pale beam coming in through the window is sunlight."

Paul had thought it was sunlight from the very beginning, but he was always impressed by all of Johnny's figures and he was relieved whenever they proved he was right. With a whoop that shook the shingles on the bunkhouses Paul tore open the office door and rushed outside to soak up that first little trickle of spring sun.

Well, you know how big Paul was. He soaked up that sun all right. He soaked up every last bit of it, and there wasn't a drop left for the rest of the spring and summer. So instead of getting warmer it got colder.

The temperature sank so far below zero it was impossible to measure it on one thermometer. You had to look at three thermometers, one under the other, to find out how cold it was.

The men found it impossible to keep warm, even indoors. Some of them let their beards grow to keep the wind off their chests. Then they tucked the ends into their boots to help warm their feet. Those whose beards didn't grow long enough to reach all the way had to walk stooped the rest of the two winters.

No one had ever seen anything like it. Everything froze. Sam put a boiling coffeepot on the stove and it froze so fast the ice was too hot to handle. The flame in the lantern turned to solid ice, and in order to put the lantern out Paul had to break the flame off and throw it out the window. When it finally thawed, there would have been a forest fire if Babe hadn't seen it get warm again. He blew on it and put it out.

Paul had already invented the Great Lakes and they froze clear to the bottom. They probably would have stayed frozen too if Paul hadn't chopped out the ice and had Babe haul the chunks to the shore, where the sun melted them when it finally came out. Then Paul put everything back in place and the Great Lakes were all right again except that Paul had to stock them with new fish.

The worst thing about the Winter of the Two Winters was that you couldn't even complain about it. Nobody would hear you if you did, because all the words froze to solid ice as soon as they were spoken.

When the cookee cried at daylight, "Roll out or roll up, my bullies!" it just fell in a jagged icicle onto his beard. The men didn't hear anything and slept all day. To get his men up, Paul had to tip all the bunks forward. Every morning he would walk alongside the bunkhouses tapping the walls, and with each tap fifty men rolled to the floor.

It was so cold that the words froze even in the cookhouse. When the men sat down to eat they might say, "Pass the salt," or "Let's have some bread down here," and pretty soon the air would be full of iced small talk. Then Sourdough Sam and the cookees would bring in the soup. The steam melted all those words hanging over the tables. They fell into the bowls and that was the beginning of alphabet soup.

Of course the men didn't like eating their words, so they kept quiet. And that was how the custom arose in logging camps of silence at mealtime.

The men saw one advantage to having their words frozen. They didn't have to write letters home any more. That was always a chore for the loggers since most of them couldn't write anyway. The Winter of the Two Winters they just stepped outside the bunkhouses and talked their letters aloud. Then they would take the cake of ice, wrap it in a sack, and send it home. When their folks or friends got it they would thaw the ice out in front of the kitchen stove and hear all about what was happening at the camp.

About the only person in the camp who could be heard that year was Brimstone Bill. His words carried their own heat. In fact when the fire in the cookhouse was in danger of freezing, it was Brimstone Bill who brought it back to life again with a couple of his most blistering phrases. Bill managed to keep that fire going all that double winter with less trouble than it used to take to make Benny behave.

Well, when the thaw finally came it was messy. All the words that had been frozen all winter began to melt. The collected babble of all those months of conversation coming at you at once was confusing. You couldn't tell where one conversation ended and another began. Besides that, it was deafening, as it would be when hundreds of men are talking. The noise in the woods was so bad you couldn't hear the trees crashing down.

To make things worse, not all the conversations melted immediately and completely. Squishy little half-melted sentences and paragraphs began settling on the loggers' shoulders and oozzing down their collars. Pretty soon everybody was sorry he talked so much.

Then thawing fragments of conversation settled on the ground and the loggers slipped and slid all over them. When a man stepped on a patch of ice he would never know if it would lie there quietly or snarl up at him, "Get your big feet off me, you oaf!" The loggers were certainly glad to break up that camp and move on.

Some folks say some of that frozen conversation still hasn't melted. When you walk through the woods today you sometimes think you hear the branches of the trees whispering. That's not so. What you're hearing are a few words spoken by Paul Bunyan or one of his loggers the Winter of the Two Winters.

22

The Popcorn Blizzard

Though Paul had three or four bad winters, he had only one really bad summer. It came at a funny time, too, because Paul wasn't logging then; he was farming. He could never get enough vegetables and things from ordinary farmers to feed the men in his camps, so he decided a Paul Bunyan farm was needed to supply the food for a Paul Bunyan camp.

What actually started him off was when he saw there just wasn't enough feed for Babe and Benny and Lucy. He look them to Iowa to forage, but that didn't work too well either. One day Brimstone Bill came in and said, "It's no use, Paul. They're still hungry."

"Why don't you send them out to forage like I told you to?" asked Paul.

"I did," said Bill, "but the trouble is they can't see the forage for the trees."

So Paul logged off Iowa and planted corn all over the entire state.

The corn grew pretty runty for Paul Bunyan corn—no more than fifteen or twenty feet high. Only two or three of the newer farmhands got so lost in the fields that Paul himself had to look for them, putting down his big feet as carefully as though he were walking on eggplants so he wouldn't step on one of the men by mistake.

Well, one day Charley, the boss farmhand, came into Paul's office blotting his forehead with his big red handkerchief. "Paul," he said, "doesn't it seem unusually warm today?"

Paul said he hadn't noticed. He asked Charley what the temperature was.

"We can't measure it," said the farmhand. "The thermometer's melted."

Right then Paul knew it was pretty hot. He went outside and all the farmhands came rushing toward him.

"What's the matter?" asked Paul.

"Nothing," said Charley. "They just want to stand in your shadow. It's the only shady spot in this part of the country."

Well that first day was the coolest of the summer. It kept getting hotter and hotter and pretty soon the men had no shade at all. Paul's shadow refused to go out when he did because it was just too hot.

The men got so dry from all that heat they had to keep drinking just to stay thirsty. The water was so parched that the cookees had to draw up two bucketfuls from the well just to get one. Even then it would be half full. And if they didn't run right to the kitchen with the bucket, the water would dry up and they would have to start all over again.

As you might expect, the heat really teased that

corn. The stalks grew taller every day and the ears got big enough for an elephant.

Then the kernels of corn grew fat and yellow, and little cracks started to show in the skin.

"What's going to happen next?" asked Charley anxiously.

"I don't know," said Paul. "But if it doesn't get cooler, whatever happens next is going to happen tomorrow."

The next day was the hottest yet. The sun was so bright that when night finally came it didn't get dark until the following dawn.

That day it happened, as Paul said it would. The corn popped. All over the state of Iowa the kernels burst. The roar made by the popping corn sounded like the bombardment of Fort McHenry.

Great puffy clouds of popcorn floated through the air and sank gently to the earth like giant snowflakes. Soon the entire Midwest was covered by the delicious drifts.

Cattle wandered into the fields and thought the popcorn was snow. Many of them froze to death. Paul's farmhands made the same mistake. They forgot it was the Year of the Hot-Hot-Hot Summer and put on their mittens and had snowball fights with the popcorn. Some of them even claimed they got frostbite, and after that nobody was bothered by the heat any more.

23

Charley and the Cornstalk

Only one of Paul's cornstalks didn't pop with the others. It was a strange one all right. It did nothing but grow. When it wasn't growing taller it was growing wider. When it wasn't growing wider it was growing taller. Sometimes it grew both ways at once.

The first time Paul noticed the cornstalk he went to call Charley to point it out to him. "You have to see this thing," he said. "It must be thirty feet high already."

Charley walked back to the cornfield with Paul and he said, "Your eye isn't what it used to be, Paul. That's forty feet if it's an inch."

"There's nothing wrong with my eyesight," growled Paul. "The stalk has grown another ten feet since I came to tell you about it."

"And another five feet since we got here," added Charley. "I'm going to climb up there and see what's making it grow. Maybe I can figure out a way of cutting it down."

So Charley climbed up the stalk and Paul got busy with something else. He forgot all about the boss farmhand until he heard his voice calling for help. Paul heard the voice clearly enough but Charley was nowhere in sight.

"Where are you, Charley?" yelled Paul.

"Here! On top of the cornstalk!"

Paul looked up and there was Charley clinging to the stalk with one hand and waving like a windmill with the other.

"Stop yelling and come on down," said Paul.

"I can't," Charley hollered. "I've tried to slide down but the stalk is growing faster than I can slide. What's going to happen to me up here, Paul? I'll starve to death."

Paul had to do a lot of figuring to get out of that one. He had to figure out how to get the cornstalk down, but before that he had to figure out how to feed Charley while he was figuring out how to get the cornstalk down.

First Paul went to the farmhouse and got his old double-barreled shotgun. Then he told Sourdough Sam to bring a pile of doughnuts into the cornfield.

"Shall I roll them out to you?" asked Sam.

"No," said Paul. "They'll make such deep ruts the farmhands are liable to fall in them and get hurt. Better have the cookees carry them out."

So the cookees strung the doughnuts along a thick pole, the way they used to at camp, and a couple of the strongest of them slung the pole over their

shoulders and carried the doughnuts out to the cornfield.

Paul loaded the doughnuts into his shotgun and aimed them up at Charley, sitting way up atop that stalk. But by the time the doughnuts had reached the spot where Paul had aimed, the stalk had grown another five feet. The doughnuts bounced off and came roaring down with such a thunder that everybody thought it was an avalanche.

After that Paul aimed about five feet higher than the top of the stalk so that the doughnuts and Charley reached the same place at the same time. Paul shot up a dozen doughnuts a day and that way he was able to keep Charley from starving while he figured out what to do about the stalk. For water Charley sucked the rain out of the clouds that passed by his head.

Now Paul faced the problem of trying to get the stalk down. Only the lead men of his crew were at the farm—Bill and Sam and Johnny. None of the loggers were there, though, because a logger has no more place on a farm than he has in a Turkish bath.

So Paul had to send out all over America to round up a crew of his best loggers. It took a while but when fifty of them had finally gathered, Paul took them out into the field and told them to make a circle around the base of the stalk.

"When I say 'timber!' " he told his men, "everybody start hacking away at that stalk at the same time. When the cut is deep enough so we can see which way she'll fall, I'll assign new positions so no one will get hurt. Fifty strong loggers can chop down anything that's grown on the face of the earth and this cornstalk isn't going to be an exception."

When the talk was over, all the men took their places at the bottom of the stalk and tested their swings. Finally Paul cried "timber" and fifty axes bit at the same instant.

But when it came time to make a second cut to deepen the first, the stalk had grown so fast the first cut was above the loggers' reach. No matter how fast they swung they could never hit the same spot twice.

So Paul had to pay the men and send them home again, and the cornstalk kept growing as fat and tall as you please. And Paul couldn't think of another thing to do but shoot a fresh supply of doughnuts up to Charley.

That afternoon he had a talk with Johnny Inkslinger who, next to Paul, was the best thinker at the farm. They talked for a while about different schemes for cutting down the stalk, knowing full well none of them would work. Then Johnny said, "If I were you, Paul, I'd forget about cutting down the stalk for now. Just keep shooting those doughnuts up to Charley and he'll be all right. Sooner or later that stalk is going to bump its head against the sky. Then it won't be able to grow any further up."

"It's a pretty tough stalk," said Paul. "Might even make a hole in the sky."

"I doubt it," said Johnny. "More likely when it can't grow up any more it will turn around and start growing down. When it comes back within reach we can get Charley off without any trouble."

"And what are we going to do with the stalk?" Paul asked all these questions because he wasn't as good at solving farming problems as he was at solving logging problems.

"When it gets back to earth we'll tie it fast to the ground so it can't grow any more," said Johnny.

"And what are we going to do with this big crazy cornstalk curving clear up to the sky and back?" asked Paul.

"We'll paint it a couple of colors and say it's a rainbow," said Johnny.

Well Paul was perfectly satisfied with this solution since he couldn't think of a better one himself. And that's probably what would have happened except that the next day a man came up to the farm in a fancy uniform with a big gold badge on it and he walked up to the farmhands and said, "Which one of you is Paul Bunyan?"

The farmhands thought it was pretty funny that someone wouldn't know what Paul looked like, so they pointed to Babe the Blue Ox and one of them said, "That's Mr. Bunyan over there."

The man in the fancy uniform couldn't see too well and besides he was from the city, so he wasn't too smart. He went up to Babe and said, "Mr. Bunyan, I have come from Washington, D.C. with an order for you from the Government of the United States of America. You have to remove that cornstalk immediately."

Babe would have swatted the man with his tail, as he would any other little pest, if Paul hadn't come along and picked him up and asked him what he wanted.

"I'm here to tell Mr. Bunyan to get rid of that cornstalk," said the little man, wiping the dust off his badge. "It needs so much water that its roots are drawing it from the Mississippi River. The water level is falling by the hour and boats are running aground right in the middle of the river."

"Mister," said Paul, "you can't complain to me about anything that goes wrong with the Mississippi because if not for me there wouldn't be any river there at all. I invented it. And I'd be happy to get rid of that cornstalk if I only knew how."

Then Paul flicked the government man with his thumb and sent him flying through the air.

Sourdough Sam was watching from below, and when he saw the man take off he said, "He's sure going to get to Washington a lot faster than he came to Iowa."

"Wonder how he got here," said Paul sort of absent-mindedly.

"Train, I guess," said Sam.

"Train," said Paul. "Train. Train. Train. That's it! That's how we're going to get that cornstalk down!"

"You mean you're going to build a track up the sides so Charley can get down?" asked Sam doubtfully.

But Paul didn't answer because he was already striding off.

Those were the years when the railroad men were building all across America. Paul walked up to the nearest line and asked for the man in charge.

When he found him he said, "Mister, let me have a couple of miles of rails and I'll give you enough lumber to lay crossties all the rest of your life."

"Fair enough," said the man. So Paul picked up about fifty-seven miles of tracks, tucked them under his arm and marched back to the farm.

There he hitched the rails to Babe and drove him in a circle around the base of the cornstalk. It took him two days and four nights. When Babe had completely encircled the stalk Paul took the ends of the rails and tied them in a knot.

The stalk, you know, not only grew taller but wider all the time. Everytime it got thicker the rails cut into it. The wider it got the more the rails cut. The faster it grew the faster it pinched itself off.

When Paul saw that the stalk was finally ready to come down he sent his men out to warn all the settlers in the nearby states. Hundreds of families had to be moved so they would be out of danger. There was plenty of time to do it because that stalk was so big that when it finally fell it took almost a month to hit the ground.

But hit the ground it did, and though the noise sounded like the earth was cracking in half, nobody was hurt by it, not even Charley. Everybody figured he would be overjoyed to be back to earth again but he wasn't. "It's true it was lonesome up there," he said, "but the food was good and you couldn't beat it for the view."

24

Paul Invents Geography

There has always been some question of just how much of American geography Paul invented. Some people like to go all the way and say that Paul invented every inch of America, north and south, east and west, up and down.

Of course that couldn't be or how would Christopher Columbus have known he discovered America when he got here if Paul Bunyan hadn't invented it yet?

No, America was here before Paul Bunyan, but it wasn't the America you know today. Paul is certainly responsible for some of the finest details—a lake here, a mountain there, the shape of a coastline somewhere else.

You already know that most of the lakes in Minnesota and Wisconsin are just Babe's footprints which have filled with water and that Paul made the Great Lakes as water holes for Babe.

The water for them came from the Atlantic Ocean.

Brimstone Bill had the watertank filled along the coast and hitched it to Babe, who pulled it to the interior. A stream of water trickled out of the tank as Babe moved along and that's called the St. Lawrence River. Before Paul put the ocean water into the holes he had dug, he ran it through a sieve to get the salt out. After that Babe had all the drinking water he needed.

A lot of American geography was invented not by Paul himself but by members of his crew. One of Paul's men—nobody even remembers the name—was driving the ketchup wagon through Arkansas once when he dozed and drove right off a bridge. All that ketchup poured out in a great long stain that's called the Red River.

Brimstone Bill and Babe helped some with the geography problem. After Paul found there was enough water in the Great Lakes to satisfy even Babe's thirst, he figured he would have enough left over to ice his logging roads.

One day Bill filled the watertank from the Great Lakes and hitched it to Babe so he could walk along the roads and wet them down. But Bill didn't put the stopper in the tank tight enough. Halfway across Minnesota, Bill realized the tank was leaking. That leak is the Mississippi River.

Nobody remembers that Benny, the little blue ox, ever did anything but eat pancakes, but Lucy, Paul's cow, once invented some geography of her own. Only it wasn't American geography; it was even grander than that. She kicked over her milk bucket and it flew up so high it got the heavens all splashed up. We know that mess of spots and stains as the Milky Way.

Sourdough Sam did his part, too. Many of the best mountains were made out of sourdough. After Paul had logged the Dakotas and Kansas and Nebraska it got pretty windy across the central plains. The folks back east started complaining, so Paul figured he would have to build a windbreak of some kind.

He had Sam fill a lot of prairie-dog holes with sourdough and then plug the holes. As soon as that sourdough started to rise the ground buckled and bulged and in a day or two there was a fine stretch of mountains they named the Rockies.

Paul invented one of his most splendid bits of geography on his first trip to the West Coast. First Paul logged in Maine, you know, and then when the pine started running low he moved on to the Lake States along with all the other big lumber men. Only they weren't called the Lake States then because Paul hadn't invented the lakes yet.

Paul thought there would be enough good timber there to keep his crew busy forever, but forever doesn't always last very long and so Paul started to look around again. His eyes fixed on the tall forests of the Pacific coast.

From where he stood it seemed that the trees there grew so close together that you would have to hack your way into the woods and then, when you chopped a tree down, there wouldn't even be room for it to fall.

Paul decided he would head west to make sure the timberland was as rich and fertile as it looked. If it was, he would hitch the whole camp to Babe and the ox would haul it out to the coast.

When Paul started out from Michigan it was still winter.

"Don't forget your snowshoes, Paul," said Sourdough Sam, who was something of an old woman sometimes.

So Paul buckled on his snowshoes, slung his ax over his shoulder and set out for Oregon.

Well, there was still snow on the ground when he left, but he hadn't gone far when the sun came out good and hot and melted all the snow. But Paul was thinking so hard about what he would do in the rich forest land of the northwest that he didn't even notice.

The sun kept getting hotter and hotter and soon it began to warp Paul's snowshoes, the left more than the right. Paul didn't realize it but because his left snowshoe was warped he began to travel in an arc. Instead of going to Oregon as he had intended, he ended up in southern California. As soon as he was aware of his mistake he headed north, but because of it he got to Oregon a day later than he had planned.

But it was during this trek to the west coast that Paul invented one of his best bits of geography. As he was crossing Arizona the heat really began to annoy him. It seemed almost as bad as it had been the Year of the Hot-Hot-Hot Summer. After a while that ax got pretty heavy on his shoulder. He began to realize what the cookees felt when they carried the doughnuts into the dining room.

Finally Paul couldn't stand the weight any more. He let his ax fall to the ground and just dragged it behind him. The blade scraped the solid rock as he went along and that little scratch is now called the Grand Canyon.

Once Paul had finished looking over Oregon and Washington and California he decided that it truly was logging country for men. So he had Babe move the whole camp out and Paul started by logging in Oregon. It was then that Babe invented his last important chunk of geography.

The ox was starting to get older and he was becoming almost as ornery as Benny had been. His appetite for pancakes swelled, and one night when all the men were asleep he broke into the cookhouse. Well, of course he didn't find any pancakes but he ate up a couple dozen barrels of flour and a few crates of eggs and some milk cans and some salt and butter, figuring that they would get mixed together the right way in his stomach and he would have his pancakes after all. He even topped it off by drinking maple syrup.

Paul got pretty worried then because he figured that if Babe kept going this way he would end up the way Benny did. So he had a talk with Brimstone Bill and they decided to keep Babe tethered at night.

"But how?" said Bill. "There isn't a barn big enough to lock him in or a lock big enough so he won't break it."

"We'll chain him," said Paul, "to the biggest rock we can find. For a chain we'll use the biggest anchor of the biggest ship afloat."

"It won't work," said Bill. "Babe is larger than the biggest ship afloat."

"I know," said Paul, "but he's lazier. And he's not too smart. Just the idea of being chained should be enough to keep him in one place. He's too lazy these days to bother to see if the chain will really hold him."

As soon as he could Paul borrowed the anchor from a navy warship and then he fastened Babe to the biggest rock he could find.

It worked for a while, too, but then one night Babe smelled some pancakes cooking in a logging camp in Canada.

That was all he needed. He rolled to his feet and with a mighty bellow, headed for the border. The chain snapped immediately and the rock rolled for miles. Now it's up in Washington and called Mount Rainier.

Babe didn't come back from Canada until he had finished every last pancake, and after that Paul saw it was no use trying to tether him. The only way Paul could keep him quietly in camp was just to be sure the ox got enough pancakes and wouldn't have to go roaming for them.

25

Paul's Just Waiting

Once in a while somebody still asks where Paul Bunyan is logging these days. The answer is that he isn't logging anywhere any more. He's sort of retired now.

It wasn't a matter of age or anything like that. Paul is like a redwood tree. As he gets older he gets sturdier. No, it wasn't old age that made him throw down his ax. It was the way logging went modern.

Fellows began to invent things that changed logging so that Paul could hardly remember he had invented it in the first place. The cruelest insult was the power saw. If a machine could bite through a tree in a few seconds, what did you need a good strong logger for?

Naturally all those inventions had the same effect on the loggers as the buckskin harness had on Babe. The men started going soft. They forgot how to handle an ax, and in no time at all some of them couldn't even shave with one any more.

After that they just kept getting fancier and fancier. They took to smoking tobacco instead of chewing it and some of them even learned how to read and write.

So Paul broke up his last camp and headed back to Maine to join Mrs. Paul and the children on the family farm. Most of his men joined the crews of other logging camps, but the ones that had been closest to Paul came with him.

To get back to Maine from that last camp on the Pacific coast Paul and Babe and the others had to cross over a good piece of America. The trail was full of memories as they recalled a mountain here and a canyon there that one of them had invented.

When they arrived in Maine they settled in the big, comfortable farmhouse and that's where they are to this day. Babe just lazes around eating pancakes and getting fat. Sourdough Sam and Mrs. Paul take turns making the pancakes for the ox, and Johnny Inkslinger keeps himself busy just counting them.

Big Ole the Blacksmith married Paul's daughter Teeny, and Brimstone Bill spends his time teaching Paul's grandchildren how to talk.

Paul hardly touches an ax any more except when some wood is needed for the fireplace or to build a new barn for Babe because he's become too fat for the old one.

Paul knows what he's done to build America and he's proud of it. He's resting now, but the first time he sees his country needs him again he'll be back.